The Glass Bead Game

Volume 2: Mercury and Hazel

Paul Pilkington

The Glass Bead Game

Volume 2: Mercury and Hazel

"OMNIA MIRARI ETIAM TRITISSIMA"
(Find wonder in all things, even the most commonplace)
Carolus Linnaus (Carl von Linné)

978-1-873818-05-3

1   Introduction

What makes things what they are?

The way we perceive them? In which case, does everybody innately perceive in the same way, or do we all learn different ways of experiencing? Do we experience languages in the same way that we experience metals or trees, stars and gods?

Is it a hidden essence which makes things what they are? In which case, is this essence a timeless, abstract ideal which we can barely even glimpse through our limited sensory perception, or is it a physical property of the thing in question – its DNA, its subatomic structure – which we can understand more and more deeply by means of that mixture of experimentation and abstraction we call scientific method?

Or is it how things relate to other things which makes them what they are? In which case, can we ever stop widening the circle of reference of relationships, and just experience a thing as it is, in its imminence? What is happening to us when we feel as though we can experience things as they are? And how does the way we think about concepts in biology, for example, affect the way we think about chemistry, astronomy or theology?

* * *

The rules of the game have been set out in *The Glass Bead Game: Volume 1: A basic form of play, genealogy, and examples.* As in that volume, it is not my intention to present original research in each of the subject domains, but to illustrate a way of making connections between these domains in a fashion close to Hesse's Glass Bead Game.

2   The four domains of play

2.1   The sign of Mercury and Hazel

The Mercury and Hazel game has four subject matter domains of play – metals, botany, astronomy, and theology. The fact that the sign of "mercury" persists across three of these domains is one of the moves within the game. But what does the sign of "mercury" signify when used in the domain of botany and trees? And what does the sign of "hazel" mean when applied to astronomy, religion and metals?

2.2   Metals and Mercury

In geology, a crust is the outermost solid shell of a planet or moon. Earth has the best characterized and perhaps the most complex crust of all the planets and moons in our solar system. The crust of the Earth is composed of a great variety of igneous, metamorphic, and sedimentary rocks. The oceanic crust of the Earth is different from its continental crust. The oceanic crust is 5 km to 10 km thick and is composed primarily of basalt, diabase, and gabbro. The continental crust is typically from 30 km to 50 km thick, and it is mostly composed of less dense rocks than the oceanic crust. Some of these less dense rocks, such as granite, are common in the continental crust but rare to absent in the oceanic crust. The average age of the current Earth's continental crust has been estimated to be about 2 billion years. The continental crust has an average composition similar to that of the igneous rock, andesite, and contains oxides of silicon (60.6%), aluminium (15.9%), iron (6.7%), calcium (6.4%), and smaller quantities of oxides of magnesium, sodium, potassium, titanium and phosphorus. All the other constituents except water occur only in very small quantities, and total less than 1%.

Since the beginning of civilization people have used stone, ceramics and, later, metals found on or close to the Earth's surface. These were used to manufacture early tools and weapons. For example, high quality flint found in northern France and southern England were used to set fire and break rock. The oldest known mine on archaeological record is the "Lion Cave" in Swaziland. At this site, which radiocarbon dating shows was in use around 4100 BC, Palaeolithic humans mined mineral hematite, which contained iron and was ground to produce the red pigment ochre. Mines of a similar age can be found in Hungary and are believed to be sites where Neanderthals may have mined flint for weapons and tools. Mercury mines dating back more than 2,000 years can be found at Almadén, in Spain.

Mercury is an extremely rare element in the earth's crust, having an average crustal abundance by mass of only 0.08 parts per million. However, because it does not blend geochemically with those elements that constitute the majority of the crustal mass, mercury ores can be extraordinarily concentrated considering the element's abundance in ordinary rock. It is found either as a native metal (rare) or in cinnabar, corderoite, livingstonite and other minerals, with cinnabar (HgS) being the most common ore. Mercury ores usually occur in very young orogenic belts where rock of high density is forced to the crust of the Earth, often in hot springs or other volcanic regions. An orogenic or subduction zone, a volcanic arc subject to many earthquakes, is created when an oceanic plate slides underneath a continental plate or another oceanic plate.

Mercury was known to the ancient Chinese and Indians, and was found in Egyptian tombs that date from 1500 BC. In China, India, and Tibet, mercury use was thought to prolong life, heal fractures, and maintain generally good health. By 500 BC mercury was used to make amalgams with other metals. The ancient Greeks used mercury in ointments; the ancient Egyptians and the Romans used it in cosmetics. China's first emperor, Qin Shi Huang Di – said to have been buried in a tomb that contained rivers of flowing mercury, representative of the rivers of China – was driven insane and killed by mercury pills intended to give him eternal life.

Mercury is a solvent for many metals, including gold. Alchemists often thought of mercury as the First Matter from which all metals were formed. They believed that different metals could be produced by varying the quality and quantity of sulphur contained within the mercury. The Indian word for alchemy is Rasavatam which means "the way of mercury".

Mercury, also called quicksilver, is a chemical element with the symbol Hg (Latinized Greek: hydrargyrum, meaning watery or liquid silver) and atomic number 80. A heavy, silvery 'd-block post-transition' metal, mercury is one of only six elements that are liquid at or near room temperature and pressure. The (loosely defined) transition metals are the 40 chemical elements with atomic number 21 to 30, 39 to 48, 71 to 80, and 103 to 112. The name "transition" comes from their position in the periodic table of elements. In each of the four series in which they occur, these elements represent the successive addition of electrons to the d atomic orbitals of the atoms. In this way, the transition metals represent the transition between group 2 elements and group 13 elements. Transition elements either have an incomplete d-subshell or have the ability to form an incomplete d-subshell. Electron configuration is intimately related to the structure of the periodic table, and the chemical properties of an atom are largely determined by the arrangement of the electrons in its outermost "valence" shell. The number of electrons per shell in Mercury is 2, 8, 18, 32, 18, and 2 in the outermost shell.

$1s^2$	$2s^2$	$2p^6$	$3s^2$	$3p^6$	$3d^{10}$	$4s^2$	$4p^6$	$4d^{10}$	$4f^{14}$	$5s^2$	$5p^6$	$5d^{10}$	$6s^2$
2	8		18			32				18			2

Fig. 1. Electron configurations of Mercury atoms in the ground state, given by subshells, and by number of electrons per shell, in order of increasing energy.

The large separation between subshells 6s-6p (6p is the subshell with the next highest energy to 6s) in Hg leads to the fact that it is a liquid at room temperature. The small separation between subshells 5d-6s in Hg leads to an unusual spatial arrangement of atoms within molecules (stereochemistry) in Hg(II) compounds.

Cinnabar is the compound mercury sulphide, composed of the chemical elements mercury and sulphur. It is represented by the chemical formula HgS. It is virtually insoluble in water. HgS occurs in two crystal forms: red cinnabar (α-HgS), is the form in which mercury is most commonly found in nature, and black, metacinnabar (β-HgS), is less common in nature and adopts the wurtzite crystal structure.

2.3 Trees and the Hazel

Any tree, with its branches reaching up into the sky, and roots deep into the earth, can be said to dwell in three worlds – a link between heaven, the earth, and the underworld, uniting above and below. Trees also play an important part in the mythologies of many societies. The most ancient cross-cultural symbolic representation of the universe's construction is the world tree. Trees are a necessary attribute of paradise in many cultures. Already, the Egyptian Book of the Dead mentions sycamores as part of the scenery where the soul of the deceased finds blissful repose. Various forms of trees of life also appear in folklore, culture and fiction, often relating to immortality, fertility or knowledge and wisdom.

Trees were a relative latecomer to life on dry land, arriving after animals. Various kinds of trees evolved separately from unrelated classes of plants, in response to similar environmental challenges, making them a classic example of parallel evolution. The sexual reproduction common to all trees results in increasing genetic diversity of the offspring. The earliest trees were tree ferns and horsetails, which grew in forests in the Carboniferous period.

Era	Period	Start, Million Years Ago
Cenozoic	Neogene (Miocene/Pliocene/Pleistocene/Holocene (the Holocene itself comprises the Boreal and Atlantic stages))	23.0
	Paleogene (Paleocene/Eocene/Oligocene)	65.5
Mesozoic	Cretaceous	145.5
	Jurassic	200
	Triassic	251
Paleozoic	Permian	300
	Carboniferous	359
	Devonian	416
	Silurian	444
	Ordovician	488
	Cambrian	542
Neoproterozoic	Ediacaran	630

Fig. 2. Table of geological periods

Later, in the Triassic Period, conifers, ginkgos, cycads and other seed plants appeared, and subsequently flowering plants in the Cretaceous Period. By the late Cretaceous, flowering plants appear to have become the predominant group of land plants, and many fossil plants appeared which are recognisable as belonging to modern families, including the Betulaceae (birch) family in which the hazel is usually placed in the scientific classification. Most species of trees today are flowering plants and conifers.

The Betulaceae are believed to have originated at the end of the Cretaceous period (c. 70 million years ago) in central China. This region at the time would have had a Mediterranean type climate due to the proximity of the Tethys Sea, which covered parts of present-day Tibet and Xinjiang into the early Tertiary (Paleocene to Pliocene) period. This point of origin is supported by the fact that all six genera and 52 species are native to this region, many of those being endemic. It is believed that all six modern genera had diverged fully by the Oligocene, with all genera in the family (with the exception of Ostryopsis) having a fossil record stretching back at least 20 million years from the present.

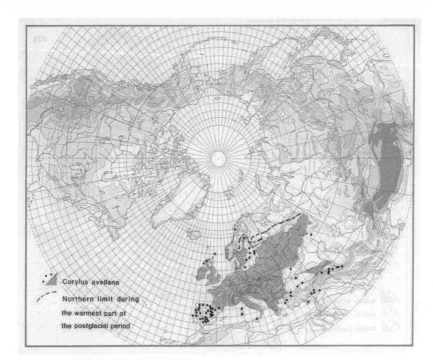

Fig. 3. Distribution of Corylus Avellana

The common hazel (Corylus avellana) is a species of hazel native to Europe and western Asia, from the British Isles south to Iberia, Greece, Turkey and Cyprus, north to central Scandinavia, and east to the central Ural Mountains, the Caucasus, and north western Iran (see fig. 3). The common hazel is an important component of the hedgerows that were the traditional field boundaries in lowland England. The wood was traditionally grown as coppice, the poles being used for wattle-and-daub building and agricultural fencing. Coppicing is a traditional method of woodland management in which young tree stems are cut down to near ground level.

The scientific name avellana derives from the town of Avella in Italy, and was selected by Linnaeus from Leonhart Fuchs's De historia stirpium commentarii insignes (1542), where the species was described as "Avellana nux sylvestris" ("wild nut of Avella").

Corylus avellana was the first of the temperate deciduous forest trees to immigrate, establish itself and then become abundant in the postglacial period. Mesolithic peoples may have transported the nuts with them as a food source, and thereby aided the expansion of the tree's range. Its sudden rise to very high pollen frequencies marks the start of the first stage in the development of dense, mixed deciduous forest in Europe from around 12,000 years ago when the last ice age ended.

The word hazel is derived from the Old English hæsl, from Proto Germanic. *khasalaz (cf. Old Norse. hasl, Middle Dutch hasel, German. hasel), in turn derived from Proto-Indo-European *koslos. Other sources state that the English name for this tree derives from the Anglo-Saxon 'haesel knut', haesel meaning cap or hat, and referring to the papery cap of leaves on the nuts; or that the English word derives from the Anglo-Saxon 'haesl' which originally signified a baton of authority.

The letter names of the Celtic Ogham alphabet are interpreted as names of trees or shrubs. For example, the letter C was associated with the Old Irish Coll, meaning hazel tree. The Latin corylus is a possible cognate, or is derived from an ancient Greek name korys meaning helmet, a reference to the calyx covering the nut,

"The distribution of the strong linguistic evidence corresponds to some extent with the paleobotanical conclusions. The hazel appeared in central and eastern Europe during the Preboreal, if not earlier, and like the alder, coexisted with the pine and birch during their long domination. Then, during the Boreal, the hazel spread sensationally. The late Boreal and early Atlantic of many zones such as northern Germany are described as 'the hazel period.' During these same millennia the hazel developed vigorously in the Baltic, the Carpathians, and along the southern reaches of the Bug, and extended into the central part of what is now [1970, when the book was published] the USSR (albeit very little south of what is now the forest-steppe boundary). From Germany to the Caucasus there were large stands and even forests of hazel trees, although to a considerable extent they also flourished as a bushy understory beneath the maple and other hardwoods. These estimates of 'the hazel period' have been made while taking full account of the fact that its pollen yield is comparatively large. Species of hazel cannot be distinguished by their pollen, but on various grounds it seems likely that the great hazel maxima of the Boreal and Atlantic involved not only the common hazel (C. avellana), but also the now more southern Turkish hazel (C. colurna) and the corylus maxima of the Crimea and the Caucasus; both of the latter regularly attain heights of over thirty feet. In the Caucasus there also flourishes Corylus caucasica. The hazel tree was probably an important food source in central Europe." "There is no botanical evidence for food production before the introduction of wheat and barley from south western Asia. Still, there is the hazel, the fruits of which are extremely common in some culture layers, and the postglacial spread of which was so rapid that [it has been] suggested that man played a part in its spread." Proto-Indo-European Trees, Paul Friedrich

Hazel has been employed by humans for a variety of uses during the past 6,000 years. White to reddish, tough and flexible hazel poles, which result from coppicing, can be split lengthways, and can be twisted without breaking. They were used during the Neolithic to make wattle (hazel strips woven into a lattice), for the construction of wattle and daub houses. Wattle fencing has been used in more recent times as sound screens beside motorways and as scenic, rustic windbreaks in gardens. Used in the past for cask hoops, basketry, hurdles, thatching, spars, sways and pegs, hazel wood was (and still is) used to make staffs, crooks, and walking sticks. It is also the wood of choice for divining rods. Hazel leaves were used to feed cattle, and hazel nuts were an essential part of the diet of prehistoric humans. In Celtic mythology, hazel nuts were believed to represent concentrated wisdom. The tough and flexible branches were considered by some to produce the worst-biting 'birch' rods (the official name, even though referring to another species). The Oxford English Dictionary (Second Edition) tells us that "oil of hazel" is a jocular name for an oil alleged to be contained in a green hazel rod, and to be the efficacious element in a sound drubbing, and that "to anoint with oil of hazel" is to administer such a drubbing.

In ancient Ireland three trees gained special prominence, the apple tree for its beauty, the hazel for its wisdom and the oak for its strength. Indeed so sacred were these trees regarded that any unjustified felling of an apple, hazel or oak tree carried the death penalty. Through their associations with beauty, wisdom and strength, the wood of these trees was often combined to make funeral pyres, at which times particular respect seems to have been paid to the hazel in relation to its wisdom, for many cases have been recorded both in England and on the Continent of hazel-wands being found in the coffins of notables.

The Salmon of Wisdom (or Knowledge) figures in the Fenian Cycle of Irish mythology. According to the story, an ordinary salmon ate the nine hazel nuts that fell in the Well of Wisdom from nine hazel trees that surrounded the fountain. In doing so, the salmon gained all the knowledge in the world. Moreover, the first person to eat of its flesh would, in turn, gain this knowledge. The poet Finn Eces, or Finegas, spent seven years fishing for the salmon. When he finally caught it, he instructed his apprentice, Fionn mac Cumhaill, to prepare it for him. Fionn burned his thumb when spattered with some of the hot fat from the cooking salmon and immediately sucked on it to ease the pain. When he brought the cooked meat to Finegas, his master saw a fire in the boy's eyes that had not been there before. When asked by Finegas, Fionn denied that he had eaten of the fish. When pressed, he admitted his accidental taste. It was this incredible knowledge and wisdom gained from the Salmon of Knowledge that allowed Fionn to become the leader of the Fianna, the famed heroes of Irish myth.

In Scotland, a hazel grove was Calltuin, (modern Scots Gaelic calltainn) and various places called Calton are associated with entrances to the Otherworld, one being the famous Calton Hill between Leith and Edinburgh, which was probably still being used for magical gatherings in the 17th century. There is even a legend that St. Joseph of Arimathea built the original abbey of Glastonbury from hurdles of hazel branches.

2.4 Planets and Mercury

Any careful and patient observer of the night sky will notice that there are certain stars whose relation to each other is perceived as remaining constant over time, though they rotate about a point close to the pole star with a periodicity of one day (corresponding to the period of rotation of the earth on its own axis). Different cultures have grouped these "fixed stars" in various constellations – the European constellations documented by Eudoxus of Cnidus (c. 408BC – c.347BC) combine Greek mythology with the star groupings used by the Babylonians. The particular group of constellations which can be observed in the night sky at any point during the year also varies with a periodicity of one year (corresponding to the period of rotation of the earth around the sun).

The naked eye can clearly observe seven principle heavenly bodies which move against the background of the fixed stars – Sun, Moon, Mercury, Venus, Mars, Jupiter, and Saturn. All of these "wandering stars" follow the same path through the constellations as the sun (corresponding to the plane within which these planets rotate around the sun). The path is called the ecliptic. The Babylonians divided this path into 12 segments, and named each after a constellation within it. Other heavenly bodies which are visible to the naked eye – comets, meteors and related phenomena – do not move along the same path, and while comets visible to the naked eye do appear with some regularity, only Halley's Comet reappears with a period short enough to be observed within a human lifetime (about 75 years).

The orbits of Mercury and Venus are closer to the sun than our own orbit, such that their apparent position to the observer from Earth is always close to the sun, and they can only be seen around sunrise and sunset. At northern temperate latitudes Mercury is never above the horizon of a fully dark night sky, though it can be relatively bright (up to -1.9 magnitude) in the evening and morning sky.

Mercury repeats the same apparent movement around the sun about three times a year with a frequency of nearly 116 days (compared to nearly 584 for Venus, and longer for the other planets). Within each 116 day cycle, Mercury is visible to the naked eye only when it appears from earth to be sufficiently far from the sun in its orbit to allow it to be distinguished. As with Venus, in one phase of its 116 day cycle it will appear as a morning star, and in the other as an evening star.

Recorded observations of the planet Mercury date back to the Sumerians in the third millennium BC. Before the 4th century BC, Greek astronomers believed the planet to be two separate objects: one visible only at sunrise, which they called Apollo; the other visible only at sunset, which they called Hermes.

The apparent movement of Mercury on its highly elliptical orbit has other unusual features which proved vexing until Einstein's General Theory of Relativity (1915) was able to explain them, in support of his theory over Newton's: "According to the general theory of relativity, the major axis of the ellipse rotates round the sun in the same sense as the orbital motion of the planet. Theory requires that this rotation should amount to 43 seconds of arc per century for the planet Mercury, but for the other planets of our solar system its magnitude should be so small that it would necessarily escape detection. In point of fact, astronomers have found that the theory of Newton does not suffice to calculate the observed motion of Mercury with an exactness corresponding to that of the delicacy of observation attainable at the present time. After taking account of all the disturbing influences exerted on Mercury by the remaining planets, it was found (Leverrier – 1859 – and Newcomb – 1895) that an unexplained perihelial [position in the orbit of a planet or comet where it is nearest the sun] movement of the orbit of Mercury remained over, the amount of which does not differ sensibly from the above-mentioned +43 seconds of arc per century." Einstein

Probably because of its rapid movement, Asiatic cultures have equated the planet Mercury with the element water, and call it the Water Star.

2.5   The gods and Mercury

Unlike metals, trees and planets, the gods are not observed in the natural world, but are projected upon it by mankind. Accordingly, religion represents one of the most diverse, fluid and variable fields of thought through time, with relationships between godheads reflected in familiar kinship and family relations (e.g. father, son, wife, twins), and it has been suggested that shifts in political power are reflected in myth in generational conflict and succession in the pantheon.

The existence of similarities among the deities and religious practices of the Indo-European peoples allows glimpses of a common Proto-Indo-European religion and mythology. This hypothetical religion would have been the ancestor of the majority of the religions of pre-Christian Europe, of the Indian religions, and of Zoroastrianism in Iran.

Indications of the existence of this ancestral religion can be detected in commonalities between languages and religious customs, mythological tales, religious rituals and beliefs, temples and inscriptions of Indo-European peoples. The names of gods are often the first words we find written in each of the Indo-European languages.

Proto-Indo-European religions have several sets of Divine Twins, which may or may not be related. Sometimes they are brothers of the Sun Maiden or Dawn goddess, and sons of the Sky god. It has been suggested that such twins may be based on the planet Venus because in stories they often "accompany" the Sun goddess, but as Mercury shares this property with Venus, and has an even closer orbit to the sun, it seems equally if not more likely that the twins are either the morning and evening incarnations of the swift-moving planet Mercury, or else that the twins represent both planets, Mercury and Venus.

For the Greeks, Uranus was considered to be primordial, with no parentage. He was overthrown by his son Cronus, who in turn was overthrown by his own son Zeus. Zeus is the Roman incarnation of another Proto-Indo-European god whose language root – Dyeus Phater, from the two linguistic roots for sky and father – also gave us Roman Jupiter, the Norse god of the sky and war Tyr, the Anglo Saxon Tiw (of Tuesday fame), and the Sanskrit Dyau Pitar.

In the current age of speed, capitalism and communication, we could suggest that Zeus has been overthrown by his own son Hermes (the Roman Mercury). Hermes was the son of Maia Maiestas (the oldest of the Pleiades) and Zeus. He was the god of wealth, profit, commerce and trade, and was also a psychopompos who conducted the souls of the dead to the underworld. It was this role among others which led Northern European scholars to equate Mercury with Wotan, who was also a psychopompos, and to make the Roman Dies Mercurii (and French mercredi) into the Old English Wodnesday (eventually Wednesday).

The worship of Mercury was the main religion of the ancient Celts who inhabited much of Central and Northern Europe in Roman times. The first written report of Celtic religion comes from the hand of Julius Caesar: "The god whom they worship above all others is Mercury. He is the one with the most shrines; they make him the inventor of all arts, as well as their guide along roads and on journeys; they assign him power over matters involving money and trade." A century later Tacitus wrote in his Germania: "Above all they worship Mercury, and count it no sin to win his favour on certain days by human sacrifices." More than three centuries after Tacitus, Mercury remained the chief object of worship for the Saxons. Matthew of Westminster transmits a speech by Saxon envoys to Britain around 450 AD. When asked about their religion, they answer, without hesitation: "We worship the gods of our fathers, that is, Jupiter, Saturn, and the rest of those that rule the world, but most of all [we worship] Mercury, whom in our language we call Voden [Wotan]." Voden of the Saxons was the same as Odin the head of the Viking pantheon.

Mercury's customary regalia include a winged cap and caduceus or Wand of Hermes, typically depicted as a short herald's staff entwined by two snakes in the form of a double helix. In addition this staff is often winged. The intertwining snakes could very well be another reference to the passage of the planet Mercury with Venus around the sun. The derivation of the word Mercury is itself unclear, but it could well share the same Proto-Indo-European root as merchandise (MERX), and be related to Mercury's roles in trading and commerce.

According to Robert Graves, "Hermes was originally not a god, but the totemistic virtus of a phallic pillar, or cairn. Such pillars were the centre of an orgiastic dance in the Earth-goddess's honour." Robert Graves, Greek Myths, vol. 1

3   Development of the game

3.1   A table of correspondences

Since part of my purpose here is to lay bare the process of constructing a Glass
Bead Game, I will explain in this chapter how this particular game came about. The
Mercury and Hazel game began with a seed quite unrelated to its outcome: the
Japanese word "sabi" which means both "rust" and "imperfection". I was
subsequently drawn into Indo-European roots to explore the relationship of the
ideas of rust and imperfection in Indo-European languages, and as well as finding
the Indo-European root **PL**AK of rust/**bl**ood and imperfection/**fl**aw, I also found that
the Semitic root S-d-y means rust and swerve.

But by now, in spite of these "tempting baubles" (Hesse) I had started to think more
broadly about iron, its origins and its properties, and found myself attempting to
refine and combine two related and equally idiosyncratic tables of correspondences
contained in Aleister Crowley's 777 (gods, planets and metals), and Robert Graves'
White Goddess (gods and trees), which produced the extended table of
correspondences in figure 4.

Latin day	English (and Old English) day	IE root of day name	Norse (and Old English) gods	Seven planets	Seven metals	Seven trees
Dies Solis	Sunday Sunnandaeg	SAWEL(N) – Sun	Sol	Sun	Gold	Birch
Dies Lunae	Monday Monandaeg	ME - measure, month	Mani	Moon	Silver	Willow
Dies Martis	Tuesday Tiwesdaeg	DYEU - sky, clear blue heaven, god	Tyr Tiw	Jupiter	Tin	Oak
Dies Mercurii	Wednesday Wodnesdaeg	WET - to blow, inspire	Odin Woden	Mercury	Mercury	Hazel
Dies Jovis	Thursday Thunresdaeg	(S)TEN - to groan, thunder	Thor Thunor	Mars	Iron	Holly
Dies Veneris	Friday Frigedaeg	PRI – to love, friend, free	Frigga/ Freyya Frigg	Venus	Copper	Apple
Dies Saturni	Saturday Saeternesdaeg	SE - sow, seed	n/a	Saturn	Lead	Alder

Fig. 4. A combination of two canonical tables of correspondences

Other columns in my extended table, from which this is an extract, included the
defining characteristics of each metal, tree, and heavenly body (with their Greek,
Indian, Japanese and Semitic names) and related deities (using their Greek,
Sanskrit, Babylonian, and Samian names), as well as the Indo-European roots of

the English names of the metals, trees and deities. From this, the four core subject domains of the present game – metallurgy, botany, astronomy and theology – emerged.

3.2   Classification systems

While struggling with the problem of how to translate the above table into a Glass Bead Game, a second idea emerged from consideration of Foucault's project to consider whether classification systems used within individual disciplines at a particular point in time are representative of more general paradigms of thought. This idea was to become the radial axis of the game. To a certain extent, such an idea is commonplace. For most areas of Western thought, we can trace a genealogy which moves from prehistory and a pre-Socratic world view, through an Aristotelian approach which remained dominant in the West until the time of the Renaissance when the Enlightenment project paved the way for empirical scientific method, which in turn has developed and transformed our view of its subject matter often through many paradigm shifts (see fig. 5).

But even before considering classification systems, the definition and boundary of things themselves need to be examined.

Objects in the natural world differ from each other, while sharing some common characteristics. For example, mercury is not gold, and a hazel tree is not an oak tree; but this sample of mercury is the same as that mercury, in a way that this particular hazel tree is never really the same as that hazel tree (at either the genotype or phenotype level). In addition, this morning star is the same as that evening star (notwithstanding varying times of appearance, phases and elongations), if I have studied and understood the movement of the inner planets and formed that particular model of equivalence – but to a casual observer on a given day it may not even be distinguishable from a fixed star or another planet. Even though gods are abstract concepts, Mercury is not Venus, but he is frequently identified with Wotan. Considering these examples together, it should be clear that though things are sometimes the same, they are the same in different ways, and also that some things can be more similar than others.

Of any particular object or experience, we might ask ourselves the following sequence of questions:
- What is this? Of what general type is this a particular instance, or does it need a type of its own?
- How can I use it?
- How does it work? How does it fit into wider groups of similar and less similar types? (It is in this phase where we test and refine theories of

classification, and of cause and effect, with a balance or pendulum between rational idealism and empirical method.)

- Where is it from? How did it get here?
- Why is it here?

At each stage, previous questions continue to resonate like organum, refining and redefining themselves in relation to developing themes.

Techniques have been developed in cognitive science for determining foci and boundaries of mental constructs in various cultures, and these techniques have been applied to subject matter areas as diverse as colour perception, spatial awareness, navigation and kinship.

At the neurological level and the cognitive level, we have a tendency to simplify phenomena to optimise our capability to respond appropriately. A need for simplification and speed in perception reduces individual objects into classes (or taxa), such as tiger or tree, and also classes which may be cross-cutting (diseased/rabid or healthy). We simplify by grouping experiences together, filtering out irrelevant details, and identifying objects with similar characteristics – like low pitch in music subsuming the perception of natural harmonics, or the same note coming from different musical instruments sounding similar. Simplification also leads to a tendency to apply classifications used in one area to other areas, for example the 7 "wandering stars" and the 7 notes in the musical scale leading to the 7 colours of the rainbow and the 7 days in the week and so on.

The use value of things tends to increase the detail involved in the taxa, and specialists in a particular subject (e.g. farmers, astronomers) can be expected to have more taxa for that subject than non-specialists.

This innate tendency, once rationalised, gives rise to ideal forms; in turn, we seek specific and general models for how various objects can be expected to interact with each other. As historical records, specialisation and empirical observations grew, former taxonomies are challenged and revised, sometimes giving rise to theoretical explanations and models which are later proven true by further observation (e.g. Mendeleev's theory of the periodic table), or which may be counter-intuitive or beyond the scope of everyday human experience, but may represent an underlying hidden reality which our senses and cognitive powers cannot directly perceive (e.g. 11 dimensional string theory). Over and above such developments, including increasing specialisation, a unifying drive persists, which is actualised and brought to the fore in the Glass Bead Game itself.

	Chemistry	Botany	Astronomy	Religion
Prehistory: The found world – sameness and taxa	The found world – things as they are	The found world – things as they are	The found world – things as they are	Personification of natural phenomena
Early historical era: Humans attempt to use and order the world by simple characteristics	Ancient ore mining, use and extraction	Ancient forestry – shelter, firewood, tools, food and other uses	Sumerian/ Babylonian counting and calendar making for agricultural purposes	Intercession with the natural world through ritual
Folk taxonomies	7 metals	7 trees of the sacred grove	7 visible planets (including sun and moon)	Acceptance of equivalences across cultures (e.g. Hermes = Wotan based on characteristics) and spread of 7 day week
The classical world: Models which rationalise and idealise	Alchemy – transformation of substances	Aristotle's (384 BC – 322 BC) division into plants (non moving) and animals (moving), and Theophrastus's treatises on plants (300 BC)	Plato – Aristotle – Ptolemy: solids, circles and models	Chroniclers and historians – comparison with little explanation or abstraction
The dark ages	Geber's (c. 721–c. 815) proposition of scientific method		Capella's 5th century partially heliocentric model	Theologians
16th century			Copernicus' heliocentric model (from 1514)	
17th century	Robert Boyle's scientific method (from 1661)	Robert Hooke discovers cells in cork (1665)	Kepler's celestial mechanics (from 1619)	
18th century	Lavoisier's law of conservation of mass (from 1789) and Dalton's atomic weights (from 1800)	Linnaeus' classification system, based on characteristics (from 1735)	Newton's celestial mechanics(from 1687)	
19th century	Mendeleev's periodic table of elements, based on characteristics (from 1868)	Darwin's theory of evolution (from 1859) and Mendel's genetics (from 1865)		Jacob Grimm's Teutonic Mythology (1887), George W. Cox's Mythology of the Aryan Nations (1883)

	Chemistry	Botany	Astronomy	Religion
20th century	Definitions based on sub atomic structure postulated by J.J.Thomspon and Rutherford (from 1897)	Molecular biology (from 1930s)	Einstein's general relativity (from 1905)	James Frazer's Golden Bough (1919-1920), Levi-Strauss's structuralism (1958 onwards)
Late 20th Century	Chemical definitions of the International Union of Pure and Applied Chemistry	Cladistic definitions of the Angiosperm Phylogeny Group	International Astronomical Union's Working Group for Planetary System Nomenclature	Cognitive anthropology

Fig. 5. The comparative development of four subject domains

Each of the tables in figures 4 and 5 represents a part of the game developed later.

3.2.1 Developments in chemical nomenclature

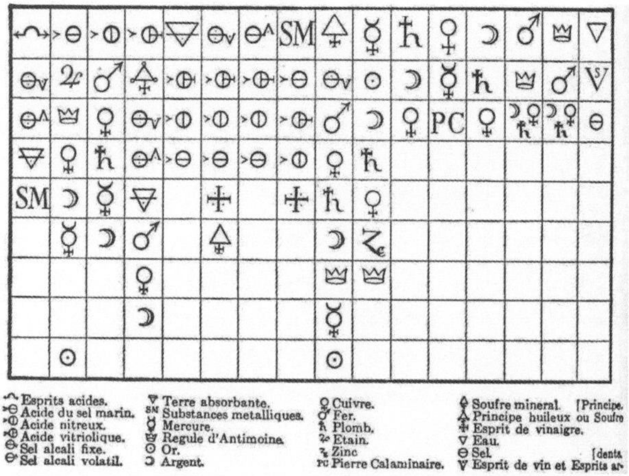

Fig. 6. Classification of substances based on their properties

Legend:
- Esprits acides.
- Acide du sel marin.
- Acide nitreux.
- Acide vitriolique.
- Sel alcali fixe.
- Sel alcali volatil.
- Terre absorbante.
- Substances metalliques.
- Mercure.
- Regule d'Antimoine.
- Or.
- Argent.
- Cuivre.
- Fer.
- Plomb.
- Etain.
- Zinc.
- Pierre Calaminaire.
- Soufre mineral. [Principe.
- Principe huileux ou Soufre
- Esprit de vinaigre.
- Eau.
- Sel. [dents
- Esprit de vin et Esprits ar-

"The activities of alchemy and of the technical arts practised prior to the founding of what we now know as the science of chemistry produced a rich vocabulary for describing chemical substances although the names for individual species gave little indication of composition. [Figure 6 shows some of the names and symbols used by the alchemists, and the groupings of substances based on their properties. The sign of mercury can be seen in four of the columns.] However, almost as soon as the true science of chemistry was established a 'system' of chemical nomenclature was developed by Guyton de Morveau in 1782. Guyton's statement of the need for a 'constant method of denomination, which helps the intelligence and relieves the memory' clearly defines the basic aims of chemical nomenclature. His system was extended by a joint contribution with Lavoisier, Berthollet, and de Fourcroy and was popularized by Lavoisier. Later, Berzelius championed Lavoisier's ideas, adapting the nomenclature to the Germanic languages, expanding the system and adding many new terms. This system, formulated before the enunciation of the atomic theory by Dalton, was based upon the concept of elements forming compounds with oxygen, the oxides in turn reacting with each other to form salts; the two-word names in some ways resembled the binary system introduced by Linnaeus (Carl von Linné) for plant and animal species. When atomic theory developed to the point where it was possible to write specific formulae for the various oxides and other binary compounds, names reflecting composition more or less accurately then became common; no names reflecting the composition of the oxosalts were ever adopted, however. As the number of inorganic compounds rapidly grew, the essential pattern of nomenclature was little altered until near the end of the 19th century. As a need arose, a name was proposed and nomenclature grew by accretion rather than by systematization. When Arrhenius focused attention on ions [atoms or molecules having lost or gained an electron] as well as molecules, it became necessary to name charged particles in addition to neutral species. It was not deemed necessary to develop a new nomenclature for salts; cations [having fewer electrons than protons] were designated by the names of the appropriate metal and anions [having more electrons than protons] by a modified name of the non-metal portion. Along with the theory of coordination, [in 1893] Werner proposed a system of nomenclature for coordination compounds which not only reproduced their compositions but also indicated many of their structures. Werner's system was completely additive in that the names of the ligands [atoms, ions or molecules bonding to a central metal] were cited, followed by the name of the central atom modified by the suffix 'ate' if the complex was an anion. Werner also used structural descriptors and locants [the position within a molecule]. The additive nomenclature system was capable of expansion and adaptation to new compounds and even to other fields of chemistry." McCleverty and Connelly

3.2.2   Developments in biological nomenclature for flowering plants

"Linnaeus wrote about dog's mercury [a spring flower found across Europe] while still a student at Uppsala, in an essay called Praeludia Sponsaliorum Plantarum, 'On the Foreplay to the Wedding of Plants.' Dog's mercury has separate male and female plants, a fact that helped Linnaeus conceive his sexual system for classifying flora. Linnaeus's system is no longer used by botanists, because by the early nineteenth century scientists considered his classifications too arbitrary, being based solely on a flower's sexual organs [see figure 7]. The modern system groups plants into families according to similarities in their leaves, stems, and flowers. This system, too, is changing. Genetic sequencing has forced botanists to revisit old assumptions about plant relationships, as species that look similar sometimes turn out to have divergent evolutionary histories." Pick

"During the 1990s, reconstruction of flowering plant phylogeny took a great step forward. Rapidly accumulating DNA sequences [...] provided new and informative sets of data. Cladistic analysis [the hierarchical classification of species based on phylogeny, or evolutionary ancestry] of these data sets was also much improved, especially through development of phylogenetic theory and application to analysis of large data sets and various methods for estimating the support for individual clades in the phylogenetic trees. The outline of a phylogenetic tree of all flowering plants became established, and several well supported major clades [a group consisting of a single common ancestor and all its descendants] involving many families of flowering plants were identified. In many cases the new knowledge of phylogeny revealed relationships in conflict with the then widely used modern classifications, which were based on selected similarities and differences in morphology rather than cladistic analysis of larger data sets involving DNA sequences or other forms of systematic data. It became clear that none of the previous classifications accurately reflected phylogenetic relationships of flowering plants, and communication about plant evolution referring to the old classification schemes became increasingly difficult. To alleviate this problem, a group of flowering plant systematists, calling themselves the Angiosperm Phylogeny Group (APG for short), proposed a new classification for the families of flowering plants (APG, 1998)." The Angiosperm Phylogeny Group

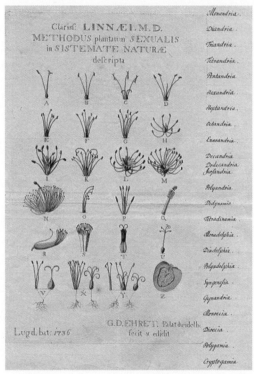

Fig. 7. Linnaeus' classification of plants based on their characteristics

3.2.3   Developments in the study of religion

Because the study of religion by theologians has been usually from within a religious tradition, there is a relative dearth of objective, scientific and empirical study of religion. Even when considered as an artefact of human kind, there is far more objective literature on the development and comparison of architecture and art, for example, than religion. Frazer's comparative religion and Levi-Strauss' structuralism gesture towards a classification based on similarity of characteristics (usually in 'primitive' societies and religion), but there is no system of religion to compare to that of Linnaeus or Mendeleev in their own fields, and no group dedicated to the objective clarification of underlying concepts and nomenclature. Indeed, "most anthropologists would agree that no constant elemental units like atoms, cells, or genes have as yet been satisfactorily established with culture in general." Kroeber and Kluckhohn (1963), in D'Andrade

However, there have been scholarly efforts directed at reconstructing the names of some deities in the Proto-Indo-European language, as well as the mythology and ritual, and its later development.

3.2.4 Developments in planetary science

In astronomy and the study of the planets, it is not so much the classification of objects which has undergone the most radical development, as the model by which the system is to be understood. That's not to say that the definition of a planet has not developed – a recent redefinition led Pluto to be reclassified from a planet to a "dwarf planet", and to be recognized as the prototype of a new category of Trans-Neptunian Objects.

The model for understanding planetary movement has evolved from empirical observation and counting of periodicity by the Sumerians and Babylonians, through the systems inspired by solid and circular geometry proposed by Plato, Aristotle and Ptolemy, to the heliocentric and elliptical geometry proposed by Copernicus and Kepler and the theory of general relativity put forward by Einstein.

3.3 The root of the tree

Classification systems which are based on evolutionary origin rather than similarity of characteristics give rise to the question of ultimate origins. Is there a Proto-World Language – an ancient proto-language from which are derived all modern languages, all language families, and all dead languages known from the past 6,000 years of recorded history? Is there an overall rooted phylogenetic tree of all known organisms comprising a single common ancestor and all the descendants of that ancestor? Is there an original prototype ancient religion which subsequent environmental changes and the human imagination have together worked into the pantheons of history, and today's living religions? Is there a single physical substance from which all things were made?

This is a seductive question for the Glass Bead Game player seeking the centre of the mandala – the "trans-category universals" which unify all knowledge. However, even if such a common ancestor could be inferred from extant languages, organisms or other phenomena, it may still only be a more recent ancestor which already may have looked back on a long evolution, and may have existed alongside other languages, organisms and phenomena of which no trace has so far been identified. Neither can we be certain that the phenomena we identify in any particular field of knowledge spring from a common source, or whether there has been parallel evolution.

Some would claim cultural trans-category universals are illusory: "During the early years of cognitive anthropology there was an idea that there might be a grammar for each culture. The idea of a single grammar from which all cultural behaviours could be generated did not last very long; the particularities of any domain quickly led away from anything so grandiose. Work across a wide variety of cultural domains in a number of cultures has found that cultural models are independent of each other. The empirical fact is that culture looks more like the collected denizens of a tide pool than a single octopus. Empirical work on plant taxonomies, colour terms, models of the mind, navigation, land tenure schemas, kin terms, etc., reveals a world of independent mental representations. Each cultural model is 'thing-like,' but all the models together do not form any kind of thing." D'Andrade

Even as far as physical science is concerned, while we may have emerged in the past few centuries from alchemy into modern chemistry, we are still very far from having a general approach which is capable of more universal results. The most abundant chemical elements in the universe were mostly produced within a few hundred seconds after the Big Bang. Heavier elements were mostly produced much later, inside stars. However, the elements are only a small part of the content of the universe. Cosmological observations suggest that about 73% of the universe consists of dark energy, 23% is composed of dark matter and only 4% corresponds to visible matter which constitutes stars, planets and living beings. Dark matter has not yet been detected in a particle physics detector, and the nature of the dark energy is not yet understood.

But though these roots in each subject domain may be hard to find, and impossible to reconstruct with any certainty, it is possible in principle that they exist. It is also possible that substantive connections exist across these subject matter domains, both at the roots, and in the branches and leaves. This is the primary subject matter of the Glass Bead Game. And if we do apply the same structures of thought to all subject domains, it may be argued that there is little to be gained from comparisons across these domains. But since diverse domains yield differently to enquiry in particular areas, such that significant advances may be made in areas in one domain which are unyielding to enquiry in another domain, then there is potentially much to be gained from seeking analogies to aid the advance of enquiry elsewhere.

4 The Mercury and Hazel game

4.1 Move 1 – English and Proto-Indo-European taxa

Mercury is to iron
As
Hazel is to holly
As
Mercury is to Mars in astronomy
And as
Mercury is to Mars is the pantheon

Not ordering or forming correspondences between the individual terms in the different subject matter domains at this stage, but merely noting the level at which taxa operate, and the persistence of Mercury across three (and Mars across two) of the subject matter categories in modern English.

4.2 Move 2 – Key characteristics of taxa

The redness of iron oxide (rust) is to the liquid state of the metal mercury and its genesis near volcanic activity and hot springs
As
Redness of the holly berry is to Hazel's sensationally wide and fast spread soon after the last ice age, and to the common practice of coppicing (fast growth and cutting back) of hazel round larger trees
As
The visible redness of the planet Mars is to the close and swift movement of the planet Mercury round the sun (just over three cycles per year)
And as
The association of (bloody) war, (red-faced) ire and the (burning red) fire element with the god Mars is to the association of commerce, travel, the role of messenger and psychopompos, and the water element with the god Mercury

All the knowledge necessary for this move was available in the iron age.

4.3 Move 3 – Paradigm of sevens

The "7 metals" known to the ancient world are to metals in general
As
The "7 trees" of the sacred grove are to trees in general
As
The "7 heavenly bodies" are to the solar system

And as

The 7 gods which gave their names to days of the week are to the whole pantheon

The "7 paradigm" probably derived originally from astronomy and possibly music.

4.4 Move 4 – Alternative signature

The Ogham letter Coll is to trees in coppice

ЙН

As

The sign of Mercury is to the space between the Sun and Venus

☿

And as

The sign of Mercury is to the winged helmet and caduceus

☿

The sign of Venus ♀ , according to some sources representing the mirror of the goddess, when supplemented by the fragment of an arc forms the sign of Mercury. If the arc represents the edge of the sun, then the sign would convey the idea of Mercury being between the planet Venus and the sun. An alternative explanation of the symbol for Mercury is that it is a stylised representation of the caduceus.

Fig. 8. The caduceus of Hermes

4.5 Move 5 – Gravegoods to protect the dead

Mercury and cinnabar's use in Ancient Chinese and Olmec gravegoods is to protection of the dead

As

Hazel's use in Ancient Celtic gravegoods is to protection of the dead

4.6 Move 6 – The doorway to the underworld

The hazel grove is to the doorway to the underworld
As
Mercury is to the guide of souls to the underworld

4.7 Move 7 – Many become one

Cinnabar is to Metacinnabar
As
Countless genotypes are to the common hazel species (though species boundaries are disputed)
As
Morning star is to the evening star
And as
Hermes, Odin, Wotan, Thoth, Nabu, Budha are to Mercury (the divinity with the role of psychopompos)

An alternative play in the astronomy domain is: 'successive morning and evening movements of the planet Mercury (possibly twinned with Venus) is to its apparent movement near the sun.'

4.8 Move 8 – Common name to scientific naming paradigm

Cinnabar is to Mercury Sulphide
As
Hazel is to Corylus Avellana
As
Mercury is to Sol 1 in astronomy

4.9 Move 9 – Phylogenetic naming

The electron configuration of mercury is to the post-transition (group 12, period 6, atomic number 80) d-block metal
As
The DNA of hazel is to the monophyletic Corylus clade section Avellana
As
The idea and attributes (e g psychopompos messenger of the gods with helmet and caduceus) of the god Mercury are to the twins in PIE religion and their astronomical origin, the helmet of the hazel nut and the phallus, and the character of the metal quicksilver

Phylogenetic naming is based on intrinsic qualities not immediately apparent (e.g. DNA, atomic structure).

Representation of the game as a "mandala"

Trees
- Hazel is to holly
- Redness of the holly berry is to Hazel's sensationally fast and wide spread soon after the last ice age, and to the common practice of coppicing (fast growth and cutting back) of hazel round larger trees
- The "7 trees" of the sacred grove are to trees in general
- ⅢⅢⅢ   is to trees in coppice
- Hazel's use in Ancient Celtic gravegoods is to protection of the dead
- The hazel grove is to the doorway to the underworld
- Countless genotypes are to the common hazel species (though species boundaries are disputed)
- Hazel **is to** Corylus Avellana
- The DNA of hazel **is to the** monophyletic Corylus clade section Avellana

Metals
- Mercury is to iron
- The redness of iron oxide (rust) is to the liquid state of the metal mercury and its genesis near volcanic activity and hot springs
- The "7 metals" known to the ancient world are to metals in general
- Mercury and cinnabar's use in Ancient Chinese and Olmec gravegoods is to protection of the dead
- Cinnabar is to Metacinnabar
- Cinnabar **is to** Mercury Sulfide
- The electron configuration of mercury **is to** the post-transition (group 12, period 6, atomic number 80) d-block metal

Astronomy
- Mercury is to Mars
- The visible redness of the planet Mars is to the close and swift movement of the planet Mercury round the sun (just over 3 cycles per year)
- The "7 heavenly bodies" are to the solar system
- ⟩○⊦ Venus is to the space between the Sun and
- Morning star is to the evening star
- Mercury is to Sol 1

Religion
- Mercury is to Mars
- The association of (bloody) war, (red-faced) ire and the (burning red) fire element with the god Mars is to the association of commerce, travel, the role of messenger and psychopompos, and the water element with the god Mercury
- The 7 gods which gave their names to days of the week are to the whole pantheon

- is to is to the winged helmet and caduceus

- Mercury is to the guide of souls to the underworld

- Hermes, Odin, Wotan, Thoth, Nabu, Budha are to Mercury (the divinity with the role of psychopompos)

- The idea and attributes (e.g. psychopompos, messenger of the gods with helmet and caduceus) of the god Mercury are to the twins in PIE religion and their astronomical origin, the helmet of the hazel nut and the phallus, and the character of the metal quicksilver

Figure 9: The Glass Bead Game in "mandala" representation

4.11 Representation of the game as a "table of correspondences"

	Metals	Trees	Astronomy	Religion
1. English and PIE taxa	Mercury is to iron	Hazel is to holly	Mercury is to Mars	Mercury is to Mars
2. Key characteristics	The redness of iron oxide (rust) is to the liquid state of the metal mercury and its genesis near volcanic activity and hot springs	Redness of the holly berry is to Hazel's sensationally fast and wide spread soon after the last ice age, and to the common practice of coppicing (fast growth and cutting back) of hazel round larger trees	The visible redness of the planet Mars is to the close and swift movement of the planet Mercury round the sun (just over 3 cycles per year)	The association of (bloody) war, (red-faced) ire and the (burning red) fire element with the god Mars is to the association of commerce, travel, the role of messenger and psychopompos, and the water element with the god Mercury
3. Paradigm of sevens	The "7 metals" known to the ancient world are to metals in general	The "7 trees" of the sacred grove are to trees in general	The "7 heavenly bodies" are to the solar system	The 7 gods which gave their names to days of the week are to the whole pantheon
4. Alternative signature		The Ogham letter Coll ⅢⅢ is to trees in coppice	The sign of Mercury ☿ is to the space between the Sun ☉ and Venus ♀	The sign of Mercury ☿ is to the winged helmet and caduceus
5. Gravegoods to protect the dead	Mercury and cinnabar's use in Ancient Chinese and Olmec gravegoods is to protection of the dead	Hazel's use in Ancient Celtic gravegoods is to protection of the dead		
6. The doorway to the underworld		The hazel grove is to the doorway to the underworld		Mercury is to the guide of souls to the underworld
7. Many become one (by improved empirical knowledge and equating of characteristics)	Cinnabar is to Metacinnabar	Countless genotypes are to the common hazel species (though species boundaries are disputed)	Morning star is to the evening star	Hermes, Odin, Wotan, Thoth, Nabu Budha are to Mercury (the divinity with the role of psychopompos)
8. Common name to scientific naming paradigm for same item	Cinnabar **is to** Mercury Sulphide	Hazel **is to** Corylus Avellana	Mercury is to Sol 1	

	Metals	Trees	Astronomy	Religion
9. Phylogenetic - based on intrinsic qualities not immediately apparent (e.g. DNA, atomic structure)	The electron configuration of mercury **is to** the post-transition (group 12, period 6, atomic number 80) d-block metal	The DNA of hazel **is to the** monophyletic Corylus clade section Avellana		The idea and attributes (e.g. psychopompos, messenger of the gods with helmet and caduceus) of the god Mercury are to the twins in PIE religion and their astronomical origin, the helmet of the hazel nut and the phallus, and the character of the metal quicksilver

4.12   Game commentary

The first move is simple, and directly traceable to elements from Crowley and Graves in figure 4. The second move shows how characteristics of redness, and liquidity/speed cut across the subject domains to produce traditional associations, and probably this represents the highlight of the game.

The remaining moves contain some interesting and credible comparisons (moves 5 and 6), as well as others which are slightly more playful (moves 4 and 7), or commonplace (moves 3, 8, and 9). Overall though, the function of the vertical/radial axis is unclear and inconsistent, sometimes vaguely representing successive paradigms (moves 1, 3, 8 and 9), but most often having no clear logic, and certainly not even contextualising the Crowley/Graves table of correspondences of moves 1 and 2 in any meaningful way.

The game's vertical/radial logic might have been improved by simply having fewer moves, though this would have been at the expense of some of the most interesting comparisons.

5 Select bibliography

The Angiosperm Phylogeny Group, An update of the Angiosperm Phylogeny Group classification for the orders and families of flowering plants: APG II Botanical Journal of the Linnean Society 141 (4) , 399–436, 2003

The American Heritage College Dictionary, Fourth Edition, Houghton Mifflin Company; 2007 – also at www.bartleby.com/61/

Crowley, Alastair, 777, Weiser Books, 1977

Einstein, Albert, Relativity – The Special and the General Theory, (trans. Robert W Lawson) Three Rivers Press, 1961

Foucault, Michel, The Order of Things, Tavistock Publications, 1970

Friedrich, Paul, Proto-Indo-European Trees, University of Chicago Press, 1970

Graves, Robert, The Greek Myths, Penguin, 1955

Graves, Robert, The White Goddess, Faber and Faber, 1948

Hesse, Hermann, The Glass Bead Game, Vintage Classics, 2000 (originally published in German under the title Das Glasperlenspiel, 1943)

McCleverty J.A. and Connelly N.G., Nomenclature of Inorganic Chemistry II, Recommendations 2000, The Royal Society of Chemistry, 2001

Pick, Nancy, Linnaeus Canadensis, www.walrusmagazine.com/articles/2007.11-pehr-kalm/3/

Rudnick, L., and Gao, S., Composition of the Continental Crust. In The Crust (ed. R. L. Rudnick) volume 3, pages 1-64 of Treatise on Geochemistry (eds. H. D. Holland and K. K. Turekian), Elsevier-Pergamon, Oxford, 2003,

Walker, Christopher (ed), Astronomy before the telescope, British Museum Press, 1996

Yates, Frances, Giordano Bruno and the Hermetic Tradition, Routledge and Kegan Paul, 1964